£5.50
UK only

Illustrated by Jeff Harrison.

Written and Designed by
A Shot in the Dark.

Published in Great Britain in 1996 by
World International Ltd., Deanway Technology Centre,
Wilmslow Road, Handforth, Cheshire SK9 3FB.
Printed in Great Britain.
ISBN 0 7498 2814 5

Sooty ™

Contents

Weekend weather

1. Sooty and his pals were watching the weather forecast on the television. "The weekend will be lovely and sunny," said the lady. This gave Sooty an idea.

2. "Let's go camping," he said. "We can drive the van to Mr Johnson's farm and put the tent up in one of his fields. "Hooray!" they all shouted together.

3. Soon they were all in the van on their way to Mr Johnson's farm. "I want to play football," said Scampi. "We must put the tent up first," said Soo.

4. Mr Johnson was very happy to see Sooty and his chums arriving. He helped them choose a nice, flat spot for the tent and gave them a hand to put it up.

5. But no sooner had they got the tent up than down came the rain! They all huddled inside the tent. "That lady on the television got it all wrong," said Sweep.

6. Mr Johnson invited them all to the farmhouse for tea and a slice of cake. They had to run across the muddy field. It was very wet and very slippery.

7. They gathered round the big stove in the farmhouse kitchen. Mrs Johnson was very kind. She gave them hot tea and buns, and blankets to keep them warm.

8. Then suddenly, Scampi yelled. "Look," he cried, pointing outside, "the tent, it's moving." He was right! It was coming towards the farmhouse.

9. The back door opened and there stood Mr Johnson. He had decided to use the tent to keep the rain off! "I thought you were a big green ghost," said Scampi.

10. Mrs Johnson turned the radio on. A voice crackled, "The weekend will be very wet and windy." "Not the weather to go camping!" added Mrs Johnson.

11. "I'm sorry," said Scampi quietly. "The weather forecast we saw at home was on a video I recorded last week, so the sunny weekend was last weekend."

12. "Never mind," laughed Mr Johnson. "You can all stay here in the farmhouse with us for the weekend." So everything turned out fine after all!

Scampi's Weather chart

Make a copy of the grid below onto a big sheet of paper. Each morning when you wake up, check the weather outside and then, in the box for that day, draw a picture which you think describes what you see.

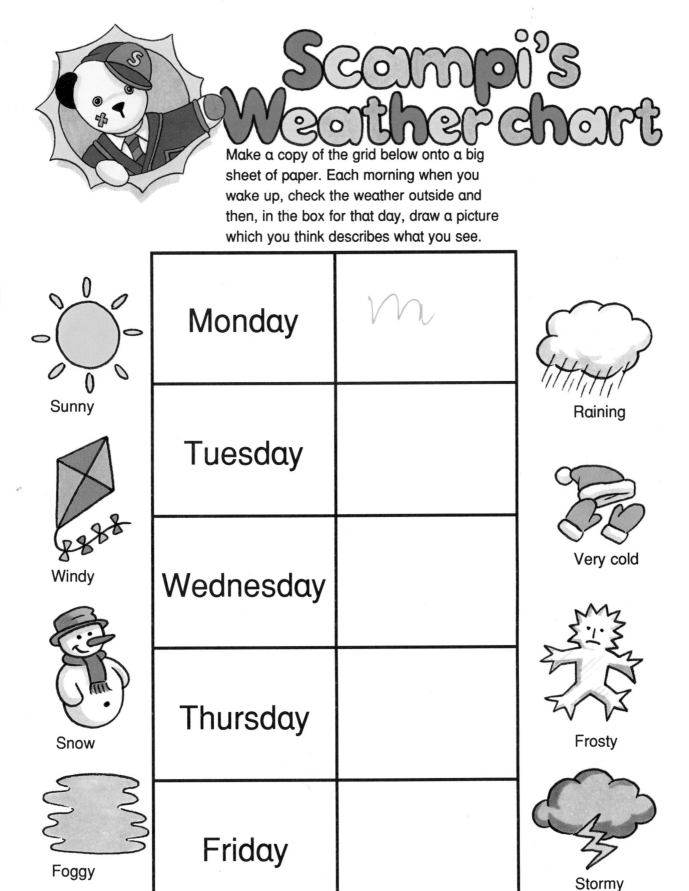

Sunny

Windy

Snow

Foggy

Monday	
Tuesday	
Wednesday	
Thursday	
Friday	

Raining

Very cold

Frosty

Stormy

Scampi has given you some ideas for the kinds of pictures you might draw, but you can have fun making up your own.

ELASTIC

1. Sooty is playing a trick on Sweep. He has tied elastic to his favourite bone.

2. Sweep is delighted to see his bone.

3. But he is unable to leave the room with it.

4. The bone keeps flying away from him!

5. Now Sooty has tied elastic to Scampi's paint pot.

6. Scampi can't understand why his pot won't stay still.

7. Sooty admits he was playing a trick on Scampi.

8. Sooty asks Scampi to help him play a trick on Sweep.

9. Sooty and Scampi help Sweep to try on his new jacket. Sweep doesn't know it has elastic tied to it.

10. Sweep thinks he looks so smart that he wants to show his jacket to Matthew.

11. But once again, Sweep doesn't seem to be able to leave the room. This makes him very confused.

12. Soo tries to have a conversation with Sweep and doesn't understand why he can't stand still.

13. Sweep arrives late for breakfast and holds on tight to the tablecloth.

14. But the elastic drags him away, taking the tablecloth and everything on it, with him.

15. Matthew shows Sweep the elastic tied to his jacket and explains to him why he couldn't stand still.

16. Sooty and Soo challenge Matthew to make a bungee jump in the local park. Matthew says, "That would be great!"

17. Later on in the park, at fifty metres in the air, Matthew isn't so brave.

18. Especially when he looks down at the ground!

19. Sooty shows Matthew the special elastic they will be attached to when they jump.

20. Sooty bravely makes his jump.

21. Soo, Sweep and Scampi are delighted.

22. Matthew is too frightened to jump. He looks for the button to gently lower the crane to the ground. But he trips!

23. Matthew finds himself making a bungee jump anyway.

24. The chums watch. They all agree that Sooty is much braver than Matthew.

Sooty

Dressing Up

Stick this page onto thin card. Next, cut out the pieces very carefully (you may need help from an adult). Now you have four fun outfits you can dress Sooty in. You might try making some other outfits of your own.

Only two of these snowmen are identical.

Can you spot which two?

Help Sweep make it safely to the bottom of the hill.

18

Look at these imprints in the snow. Can you tell who or what has made them?

S _ _ _ y   S _ _ _ p   S _ _   S _ _ _ _ i

The gang have made snow models of themselves. Do you think you can tell who's who?

Soo's snowbear

One morning Sooty looked out of his window to find the world covered in snow! He called his chums to come and see.

"Wow!" said Scampi. "Now we can go sledging and have snowball fights!"

They were all very excited and started running around the house looking for boots, hats, gloves and scarves, and of course their sledges.

"I don't want a snowball fight," said Soo. "There's only one thing I want to do – I want to build a snowbear."

Sooty was ready first. He opened the front door and stared in amazement. The snow had fallen so heavily that the garden was completely buried!

"I don't think we will be going anywhere today," he said. "At least not until we have cleared the path."

They put their sledges down and Soo found each of the boys a shovel. "You clear the snow," she said, "while I make some lunch."

Sooty and Scampi set to work straight away shovelling the thick snow to the sides of the path. It was jolly hard work.

Sweep watched for a while and then he had an idea. He took his shovel and started piling snow onto his sledge. Then, when it was full, he pulled the sledge through the house and emptied the snow into the back yard!

He carried on, thinking how clever he was, until Soo came out of the kitchen, tripped over the sledge and sent snow everywhere! She was very cross.

"What a silly idea to bring snow through the house!" she said. They cleared it up quickly before it began to melt.

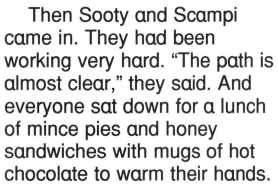

Then Sooty and Scampi came in. They had been working very hard. "The path is almost clear," they said. And everyone sat down for a lunch of mince pies and honey sandwiches with mugs of hot chocolate to warm their hands.

After a well-earned rest they set to work again.

"I can't wait to make my snowbear," said Soo.

This time Sweep worked especially hard to make up for his mistake. He shovelled away, tossing the snow over his shoulder as fast as he could.

"Hooray!" shouted Scampi when they reached the garden gate.

"Come on," said Sweep. "Let's find our sledges and go."

They called out to Soo, but

there was no answer.

Then they noticed a snowbear standing right in the middle of the pathway they had just cleared!

"Well," said Sweep. "It looks as though Soo has had fun building her snowbear while we were doing all the hard work."

But then they watched in amazement as the snowbear started to shiver and shake. Then it gave out a huge sneeze – "Atishoo!"

The snow fell away and

underneath was Soo!

Poor Soo! The boys had been shovelling so quickly without looking behind them that when she came out to help she had been covered in snow!

"Come on," said Sooty. "We can go sledging tomorrow. Today we should all help Soo build a real snowbear."

And that is just what they did.

Sledge Race

This is a game for up to four players.
Decide who you are going to be: Sooty, Sweep, Soo or Scampi.
You need to throw a six to pick up your sledge and then you can start.
Follow the route and obey the instructions when you land on them.
Drive carefully, and good luck!

START

1

2

The string of your sledge has snapped. Start again.

3

4

5

6

Hit a tree stump. Go back 2.

7

8

9

10

Stop to build a snowman. Miss a turn.

11

12

13

14

Hit by a snowball. Go back 2.

15

Skid on ice. Go on 4.

16

17

Throw an even number to go over the bridge.

18

Well done!

25

Too busy

1. Scampi was in the back yard, playing football, when he saw Soo through the kitchen window. He asked her if she would play football with him.

2. Soo was making a cake. "I'm too busy," she said. Scampi came inside. "I could help you make your cake," he said, putting his ball down on the floor.

3. Before Soo had a chance to stop him, Scampi had grabbed the basin which was full of cake mix. "Splosh!" It went all over Soo and all over the floor.

4. Soo was very cross. She chased Scampi out of the kitchen and back into the yard. She threw his ball after him, and told him to stop being a nuisance.

5. Sweep was busy cleaning the windows. Scampi asked if he could help. Sweep said he was too small to climb the ladder. It was dangerous and he might fall.

6. So Scampi played football again. But, oh dear! The ball bounced over his head and knocked Sweep's ladder. He lost his balance and fell – splash!

7. Now Sweep was very cross. "Keep that ball away from me," he said to Scampi. "Go and play at the bottom of the yard out of harm's way." Poor Scampi.

8. Sooty came through the back gate, carrying two heavy bags. "Will you play football, Sooty?" asked Scampi. "Sorry," said Sooty, "I have to unpack these."

9. Scampi wanted to help. He grabbed one of the bags – it split! The groceries spilled all over the yard. "Oh, Scampi – look what you've done!" said Sooty crossly.

10. Scampi was very upset. He only wanted someone to play football with him, but everyone was too busy. And when he tried to help things kept going wrong.

11. Sooty decided the safest thing to do was for them all to play football together. So they did. Soo was the referee. "Goal!" shouted Scampi.

12. After the match, Scampi was so tired he fell asleep in Sooty's big armchair. "I think it's safe for us to finish our jobs now," smiled Sooty.

CaptainSweep

How to make a super-hero costume

You can be a superhero just like Captain Sweep, with your very own superhero costume. It's cheap and easy to make, but you will need an adult's help.

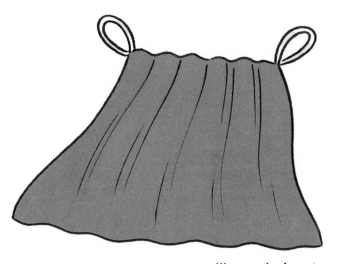

1. Use the mask template above as a guide for shape and size. Cut the mask shape out of black card. Use thin elastic for the strap. The holes for the strap can be made with a nail. You must ask an adult to help!

2. To make the superhero shirt you will need an old T-shirt. White is best.
Using fabric paint or acrylic paint, paint a circle on the front of the T-shirt. Next, paint the first letter of your first name in the centre of the circle. That's all there is to it. Leave it to dry.
If you have a pair of shorts that match the paint colour you have chosen, then you could wear them, but any shorts will do. You are almost ready!

3. For the cape you will need about one yard of material. Make an elastic loop on two of the corners for your arms to go through. Now you are ready to save the world!

29

Sweep

Copy and Colour

Copy the picture of Sweep playing his favourite instrument, the drums, into the grid below, and then colour it in. You don't have to use the same colours, just have fun!

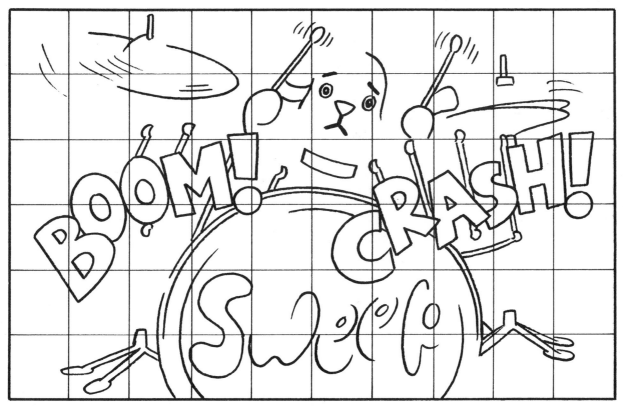

Home Alone

1. Matthew, Sooty and Co. are preparing to go away for the weekend. Sweep is very excited.

2. Sweep tells Soo how excited he is.

3. Matthew carefully packs his suitcase.

4. But he forgets to fasten it properly and everything falls out!

5. Sooty decides to pack all his toys into a magic suitcase. Suddenly the suitcase bursts open. Sooty's magic spell must have worn off.

6. Scampi wants to take his mice with him, but the mice don't want to be packed.

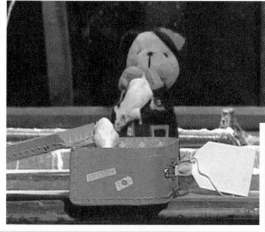

7. Sweep packs sensible clothes and of course his favourite bone.

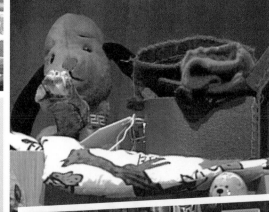

8. At last they are ready to go. Matthew locks the door.

9. Sweep is so excited that he needs to go to the toilet again. Matthew rushes in to the kitchen to check the gas is turned off.

10. In their confusion, they set off without Sweep!

11. Sweep realises it is very quiet. He searches the house for the others.
He looks in the bedroom first.

12. He looks everywhere, even upstairs in the loft. He can't find them.

13. Poor Sweep. He realises he has been left behind.

14. Sweep wonders if the others are missing him. Or perhaps they left him behind on purpose.

15. Sweep decides to make the most of being home alone. He has a slap-up meal of all his most favourite foods.

16. Outside it is getting dark. Suddenly Sweep hears a loud noise from the back yard.

17. It was Matthew, knocking over a dustbin. They have come back for Sweep after all. But Matthew can't find his door key.

18. Sooty climbs up the ladder to an upstairs window.

19. Sweep thinks it's burglars, and he pushes the ladder away. Sooty lands in a dustbin!

20. Sweep gets a bowl of water to soak the intruders.

21. The water lands right on top of Matthew's head, making him very wet.

22. Matthew puts his hand through the letter box to reach the spare key.

23. Sweep is ready for him and paints his hand with blue paint.

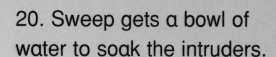

24. Sooty, Scampi and Soo tell Matthew to hurry up; Sweep must be frightened.

25. Matthew finally finds the key and goes in.

26. He walks straight into Sweep's tripwire and goes head first into a bowl of paint.

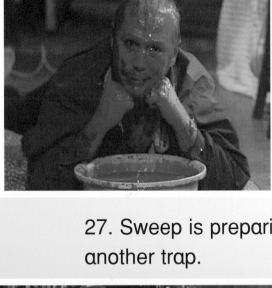

27. Sweep is preparing another trap.

28. Suddenly Matthew is upside down and caught in a net.

29. Soo tells Sweep how clever he has been to defend the shop. But Matthew doesn't agree!

Oh dear! In their rush to go away on holiday, the chums have got their cases mixed up. Perhaps you can sort out whose case is whose? There are some give-away clues.

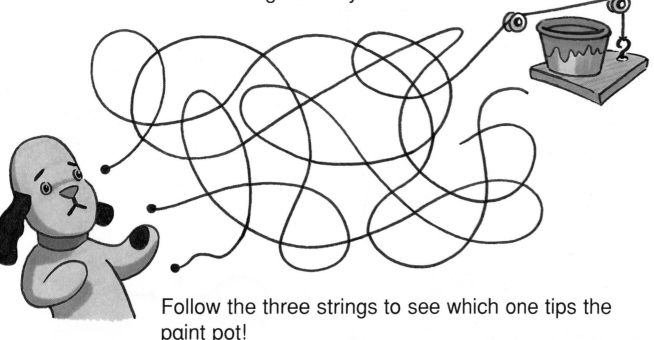

Follow the three strings to see which one tips the paint pot!

Soo's Snapshots

Soo loves to take pictures with her camera. The only trouble is, she isn't very quick, and she often misses the action she wants to snap. Here are some of her 'not-so-quick' snapshots.

Sooty pulling a rabbit out from his hat.

Sweep building a beautiful sandcastle.

Scampi trying
out his new
roller skates.

Scampi making
his first dive into
the pool.

Sooty giving
a display on
his trampoline.

41

Soo

Shopping Mix-up

debra   _____

imlk   _____

eseche   _____

gesg   _____

trebut   _____

reclea   _____

thaloocec   _____

sneba   _____

spleap   _____

gresoan   _____

snabaan   _____

guassase   _____

acnob   _____

frulo   _____

yehno   _____

Soo is going shopping, but cheeky Scampi has muddled up her shopping list. Can you unscramble the items for her?

Captain Sweep

Sweep sat on the edge of his bed, watching his favourite television hero – Flash the Wonder Dog. The fastest, most fearless dog in the whole world.

When the programme finished Sweep had a great idea.

"That's it!" he said out aloud. "I want to be just like Flash. I'm going to become a superdog!" And he went downstairs to put his plan into action.

First he saw Soo doing some sewing. "Could I have some of your material?" he asked. "I'm going to be a superhero and I need to make a costume.

Soo giggled and gave Sweep some material.

Next he decided he should practise doing what superheroes do before he could become one himself.

So he practised jumping over obstacles.

He practised swinging on ropes. He practised aiming his waterpistol. And, he tried on his goggles and flippers in case he had to rescue someone under water.

Training to be a superhero was very tiring. So Sweep decided to take a rest in his room and finish making his costume.

Meanwhile, Sooty, Soo and Scampi were working hard in the garden. It was a warm, bright day and there were lots of jobs that needed doing.

Suddenly a masked figure appeared as if from nowhere.

"Is it a dog?" said Sooty.

"Is it a bone?" said Scampi.

"No," said Soo. "It's Captain Sweep!"

"Greetings friends," said Captain Sweep. He looked at Soo. "Don't be afraid!" he said. "I am Captain Sweep, defender of the weak. The most fearless dog in the whole world. Tell me how I can help you."

"Well," said Soo. "I am trying to build a rockery but the rocks are very heavy."

"Then it's a job for Captain Sweep!" said the masked stranger. "I have the strength of ten dogs. Just show me where you want the rocks. I'll take care of things."

So Sweep, disguised as Captain Sweep, began moving the rocks one by one to a new spot at the other end of the garden. They were very heavy. It was hard work and he soon began to feel hot.

"Excuse me Sweep – I mean Captain Sweep," said Soo. "Do superheroes drink orange squash?" She held out a beaker.

"That's very kind of you ma'am," said Captain Sweep. He took the beaker and drank the squash in seconds.

"Wow!" said Scampi. "You must be the fastest drinker in the whole world."

"It was nothing, my boy," said Captain Sweep. "Now, how can I help you?"

"I have to mow the lawn, but the mower is too big and heavy for me," said Scampi.

"Stand back! This is another job for Captain Sweep!" said the masked hero.

And he began to mow the lawn, his cape billowing in the wind.

The lawnmower was very stiff and Captain Sweep soon began to feel tired and hungry.

"Do superheroes eat apple pie and honey sandwiches?" asked Soo, holding out a plate.

"We usually eat supercharged spaghetti," said Captain Sweep. "I don't suppose you have any, do you? Never mind, the apple pie and sandwiches will do."

Within a flash Sweep had eaten all the pie and all the sandwiches!

"Wow!" said Sooty. "You must be the fastest eater in the whole world."

"Thank you sir," said Captain Sweep. "Now, what can I do for you?"

Sooty pointed to a large pile of straw. "I need to move all that straw into the garden shed, but my fork is broken," he said.

"Never fear – Captain Sweep is here!" said the superhero, and he set to work carrying armfuls of straw to the shed.

After a while Sooty noticed that Sweep had disappeared. He asked Soo and Scampi if they had seen him. When they both said they hadn't he organised a search.

Everyone set off in different directions.

A few minutes later there was a cry from Scampi. "Quick! In the shed. I've found something!"

Soo and Sooty ran to the shed, and sure enough, there, dozing peacefully in the pile of straw, was Sweep.

"He will have to change his name from now on," laughed Scampi, "to Captain Sleep!"

Road Sign Quiz

No cycling

Loose chippings on the road

No overtaking

No entry

No parking

Work in progress

Look at these road signs very carefully. Try to remember them...

Cover up the previous page.
Now write in what you think the signs
mean in the spaces below each sign.

Now check your answers.
How did you do?

A Trip To The Park

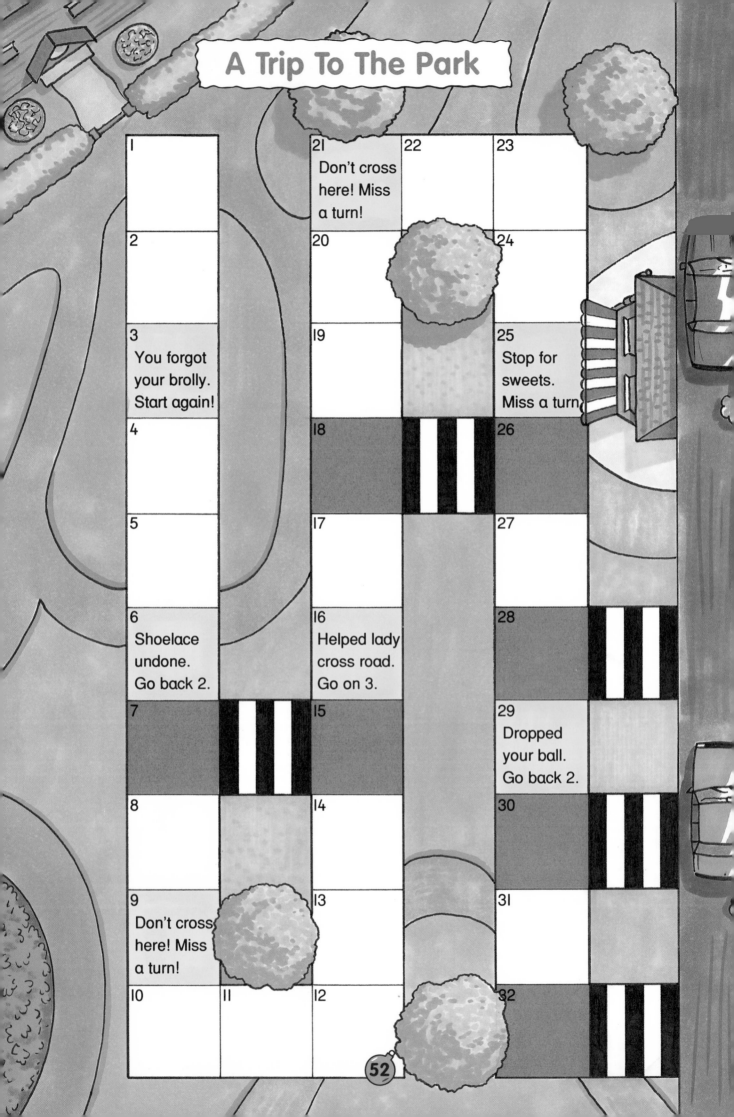

1

2

3
You forgot
your brolly.
Start again!

4

5

6
Shoelace
undone.
Go back 2.

7

8

9
Don't cross
here! Miss
a turn!

10

11

12

13

14

15

16
Helped lady
cross road.
Go on 3.

17

18

19

20

21
Don't cross
here! Miss
a turn!

22

23

24

25
Stop for
sweets.
Miss a turn

26

27

28

29
Dropped
your ball.
Go back 2.

30

31

32

52

This is a game for up to 4 players. Decide who goes first. Start from the house and follow the route. You must obey the instructions if you land on a yellow square. If you land on a red square you can go over the crossing or under the motorway. The first player to reach the park safely is the winner.

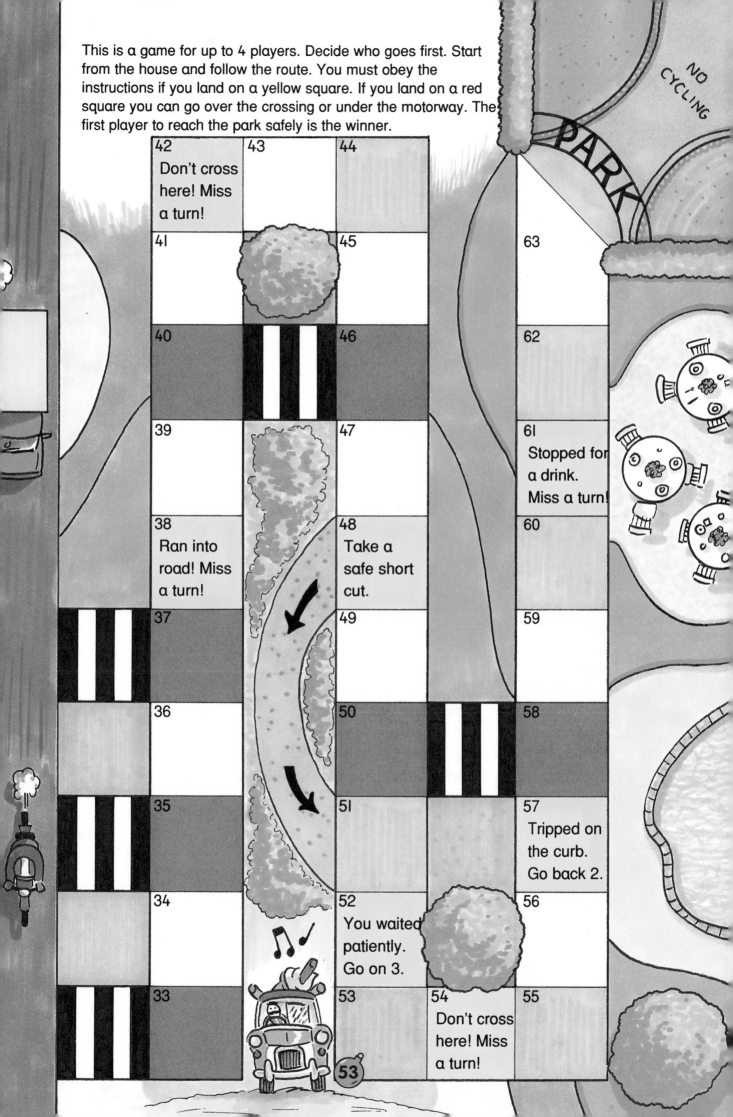

42 Don't cross here! Miss a turn!	43	44
41		45
40		46
39		47
38 Ran into road! Miss a turn!		48 Take a safe short cut.
37		49
36		50
35		51
34		52 You waited patiently. Go on 3.
33	53	54 Don't cross here! Miss a turn!

63
62
61 Stopped for a drink. Miss a turn!
60
59
58
57 Tripped on the curb. Go back 2.
56
55

PARK

NO CYCLING

Scampi

Scampi's lost balls..

As you know, Scampi loves to play football.
He is always losing his balls over his neighbour's
hedge. His neighbour has kindly let him into his back
yard to fetch all the balls he has kicked over the hedge.
There are ten balls in all.
Help Scampi to find them.

Christmas Activity Puzzles

Colour in the dotted shapes to reveal some Christmas treasures.
A star. A cracker. A tree and a present.

Draw the two missing halves of these jolly Christmas characters.
Then, colour your drawing in to complete the pictures.

Here's your chance to help put the colour into Sooty's Christmas tree. Look at all those lovely presents!

Christmas magic

1. It was Christmas Eve. Sooty was decorating the Christmas tree. He had found a beautiful gold star. He reached up and put it right on the very top.

2. Soo had put all the Christmas cards on strings hanging above the fireplace. She tried to count them all but there were so many, she lost count.

3. "Look what we've found," said Sweep. He and Scampi were both holding two large Christmas stockings. "There's one for each of us," said Scampi.

4. When all the stockings were hanging from the mantelpiece, Sooty told the others it was time for bed. "Father Christmas will be here very soon," he said.

5. As soon as Soo, Scampi and Sweep had gone up to bed, Sooty went to look for his magic wand. "It's time to create some Christmas magic," he said.

6. But, oh dear – Sooty's wand had gone missing. "What will I do?" he said to himself. "I haven't wrapped any presents, and the lights are still in their box."

7. Sooty looked everywhere for his magic wand, but he was out of luck. It was nearly midnight. "The others will be so upset," he thought. "But I must go to bed."

8. Sooty woke up very early. He wanted to sort things out before his chums got out of bed. But wait – he could hear voices laughing downstairs.

9. Sooty was still coming down the stairs when Soo ran to meet him. "Merry Christmas," she smiled. "And thank you." She gave him a huge hug.

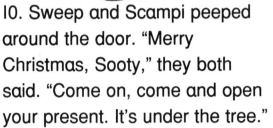

10. Sweep and Scampi peeped around the door. "Merry Christmas, Sooty," they both said. "Come on, come and open your present. It's under the tree."

11. When Sooty saw the living room he couldn't believe his eyes! The decorations were all up, and the lights glittered around the room. It was wonderful.

12. Sooty sat in his favourite chair, holding a large Christmas parcel. He was very puzzled. But we all know who puts the real magic into Christmas – don't we?

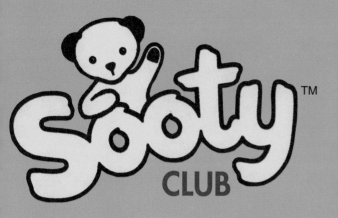

Join the new Sooty Club – it's magic!

When you become a member of the Sooty Club you'll get a personal letter from Sooty and his friends, a membership card and a badge with **your** name on. You'll love the video of **Bubble Trouble**, a brilliant Sooty show now available **only** to Club Members. Not to mention two great face masks...two finger puppets...a Sooty story...a bookmark...and a giant Sooty colouring book. There's even a rainbow pencil disguised as Sooty's wand and a Sooty conjuring trick to amaze your friends. Magic!

And that's not all. We'll also send you the next available issue of the Sooty magazine as soon as it comes out. And on your birthday, and again at Christmas, you'll receive great greetings cards.

If all this could be bought in the shops it would cost well over £12.00, but a year's membership is superb value at just £8.99 (plus 89p postage). There's a 14-day no quibble money-back guarantee if you're not delighted!

Izzy wizzy, let's get busy!

Simply return the coupon below to: **Sooty Club, TV Town (Dept. WI), PO Box 142, Horsham, RH13 5FJ. Or call: 01403 242727 to pay by credit card.**

Please note: We reserve the right to change the terms of this offer (including the contents of the Welcome Pack) at any time, but we offer a 14 day no quibble money-back guarantee. We do not sell directly to children - all communications (except the Welcome Pack) will be via parents/guardians. After 30/6/97 please call to check that the price is still valid. Allow 28 days for delivery. Promoter: Robell Media Promotions Limited, registered in England number 2852153. Sooty™ and © 1996 Sooty International Limited. Licensed by Chatsworth Enterprises.

Please enrol the following as a member of the Sooty Club (block capitals):

Child's Full Name: _____   Child's Address: _____

_____   Post Code: _____   Date of Birth: __/__/__

Your Name: _____   Address (if different): _____

_____ Post Code: _____   Name of child's parent or guardian (if not you): _____

☐ I enclose a cheque or postal order for £9.88 (£8.99 + £0.89 postage) payable to **Sooty Club**.

☐ Please charge the sum of £9.88 to my Access/Visa account.

Card number: ☐☐☐☐ ☐☐☐☐ ☐☐☐☐ ☐☐☐☐ ☐☐☐   Expiry Date: __/__   **WI**